Dear **BIG SISTER,**

You are going to be a great sibling! Your baby brother will be your new best friend. You will share lots of hugs, laughs, and great times.

When the baby is born, things will change a little in your house. But one thing that will never change is how much you are **LOVED!**

Congratulations on your
new baby brother!
Welcome home baby!

Your baby will have tiny toes, feet, and fingers.

BABY

WEIGHT: ____

HEIGHT: ____

And itty-bitty clothes.

Mommy and Daddy may be extra
tired after the new baby comes!

Before you touch your baby brother,
please wash your hands with soap.

Babies like to sleep.

Babies like to eat.

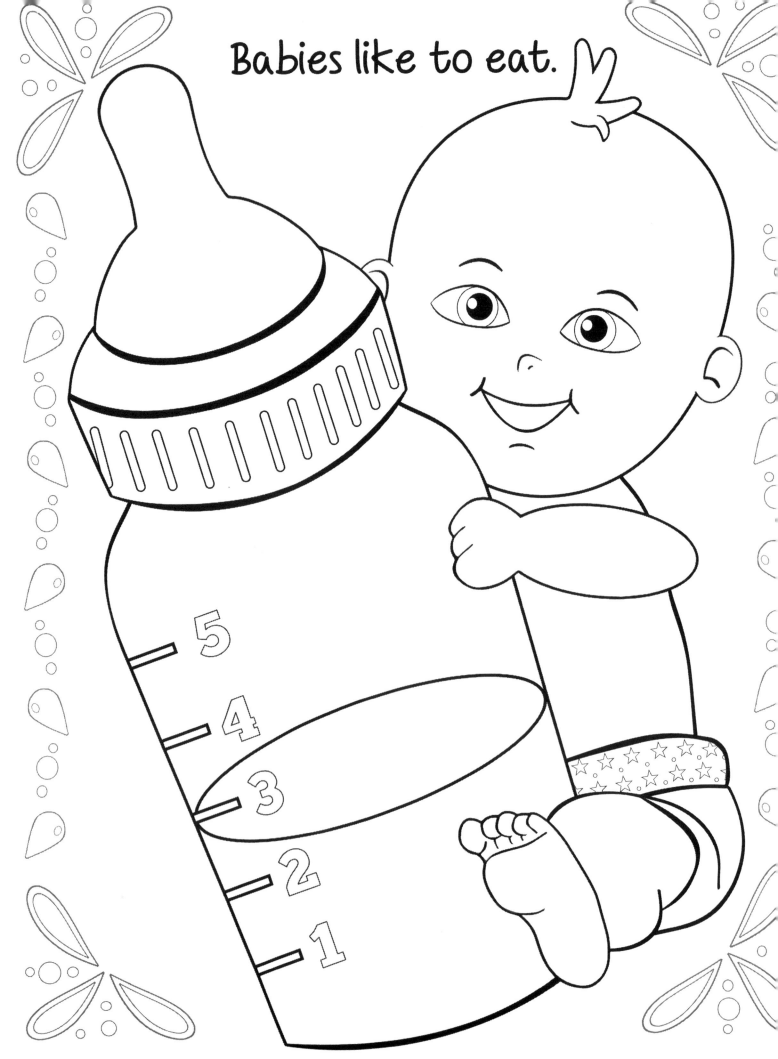

Babies like to cry.

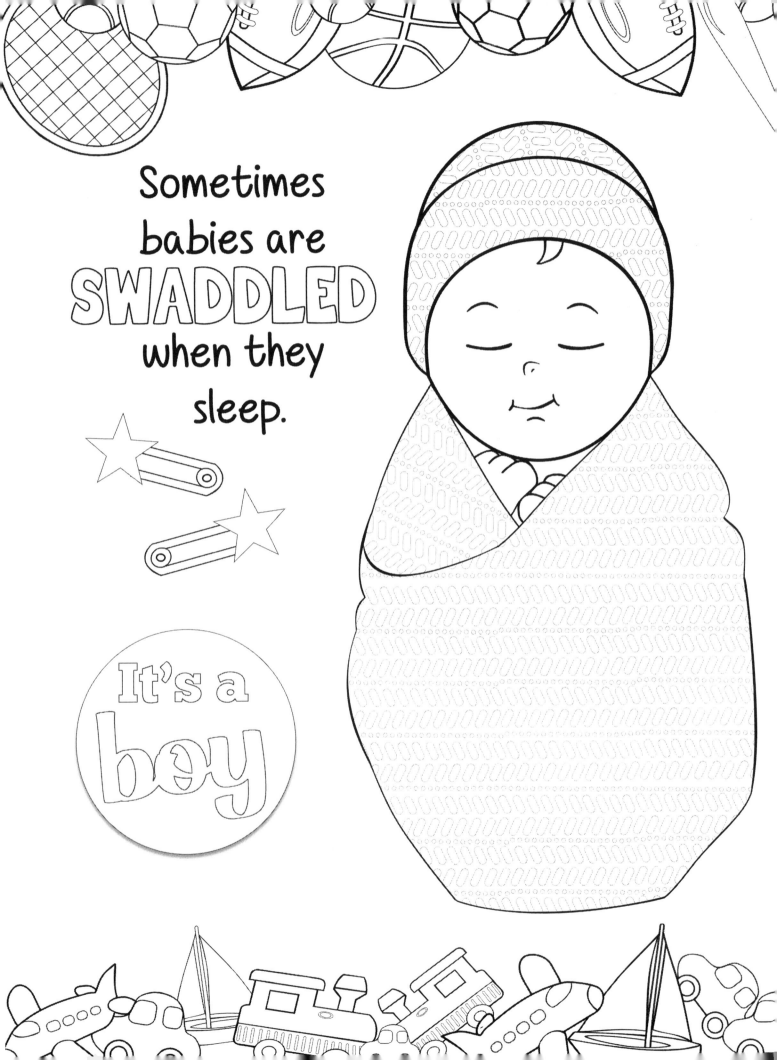

Sometimes babies are **SWADDLED** when they sleep.

It's a boy

Some babies
listen to lullabies
while they sleep.

Some babies like pacifiers to make them feel better.

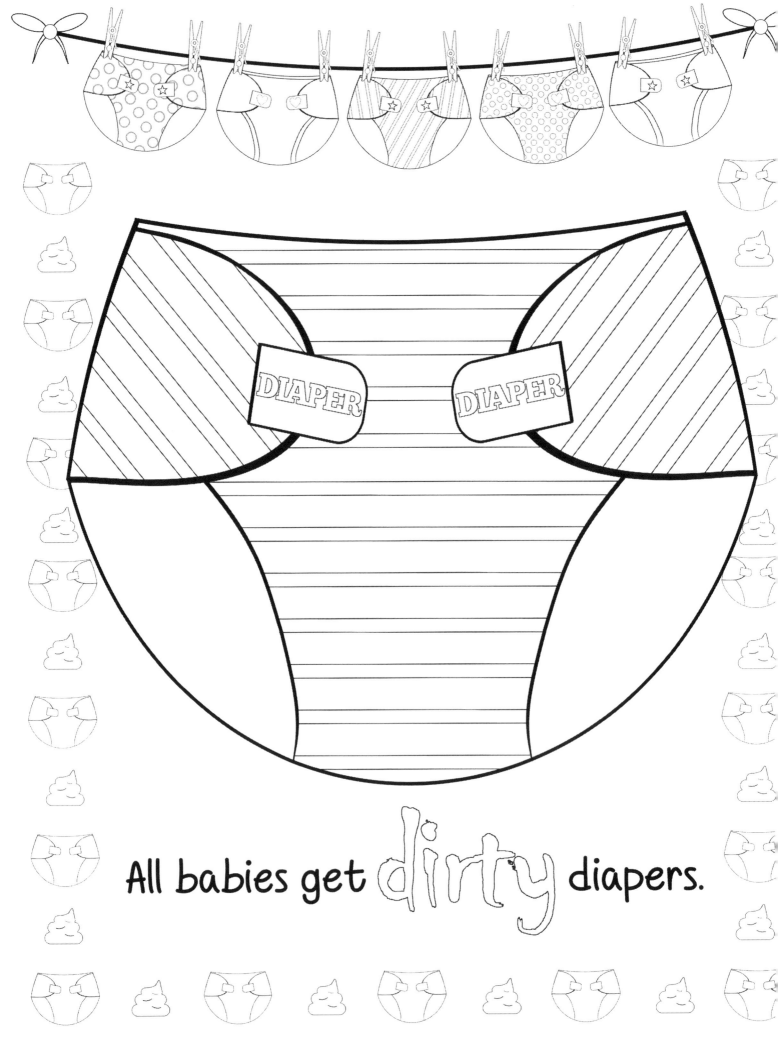

All babies get dirty diapers.

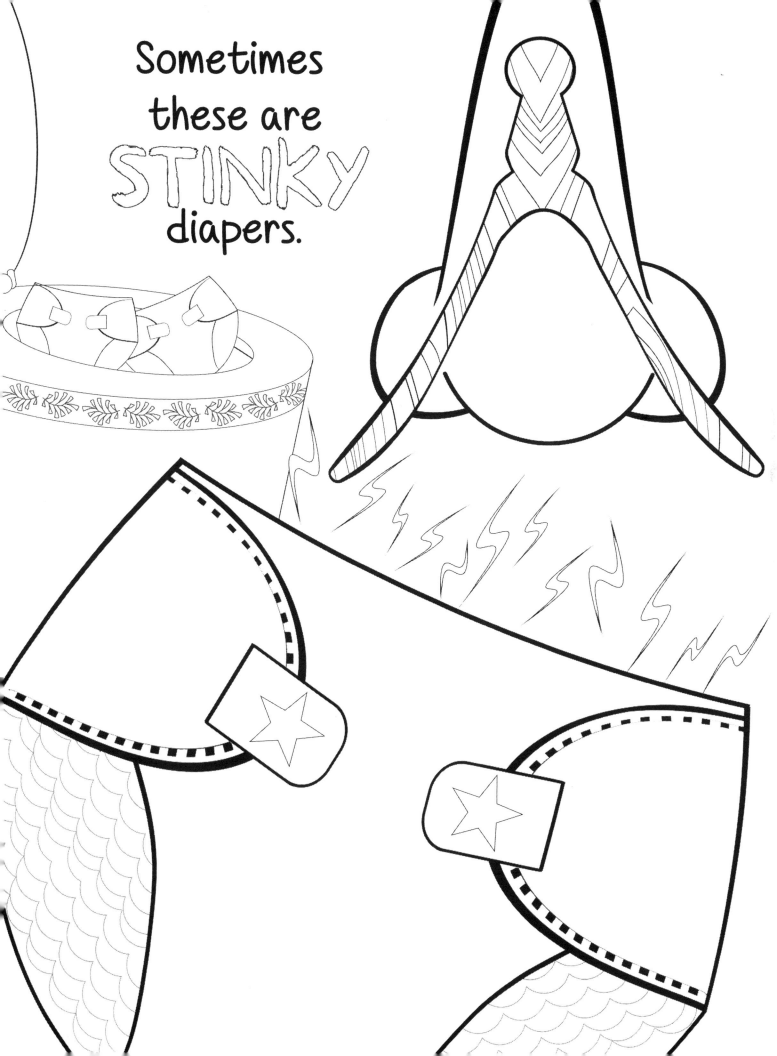

Sometimes these are
STINKY
diapers.

Your baby brother will get a fresh diaper on his changing table.
He may cry and fuss.

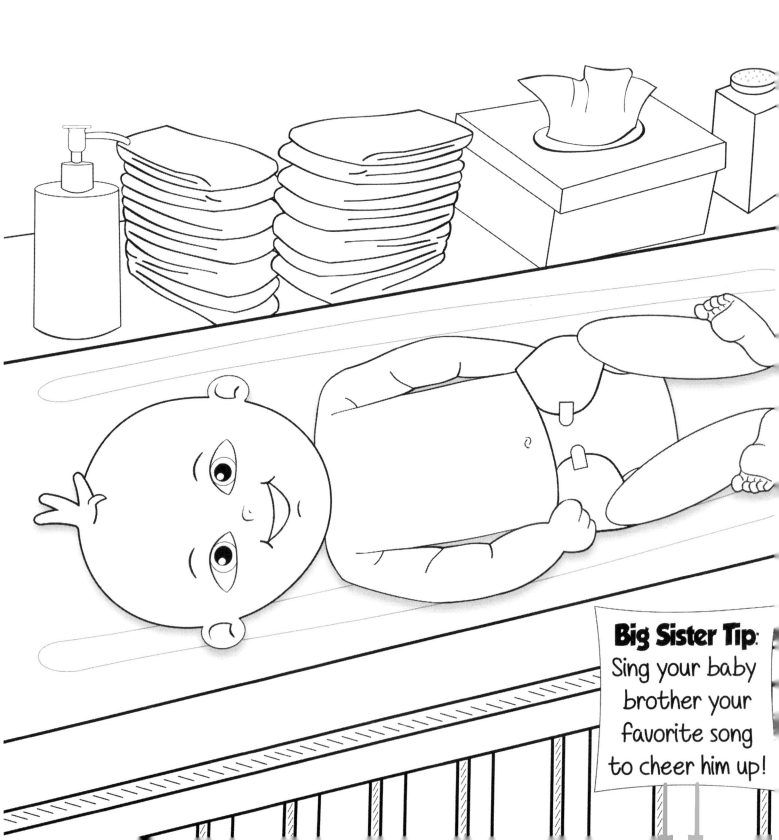

Big Sister Tip: Sing your baby brother your favorite song to cheer him up!

Babies do TUMMY TIME for exercise.

Babies like to
SWING
and
BOUNCE.

Babies like to ride in the STROLLER.

You can play games with your baby brother. Babies like to play
PEEK-a-BOO,

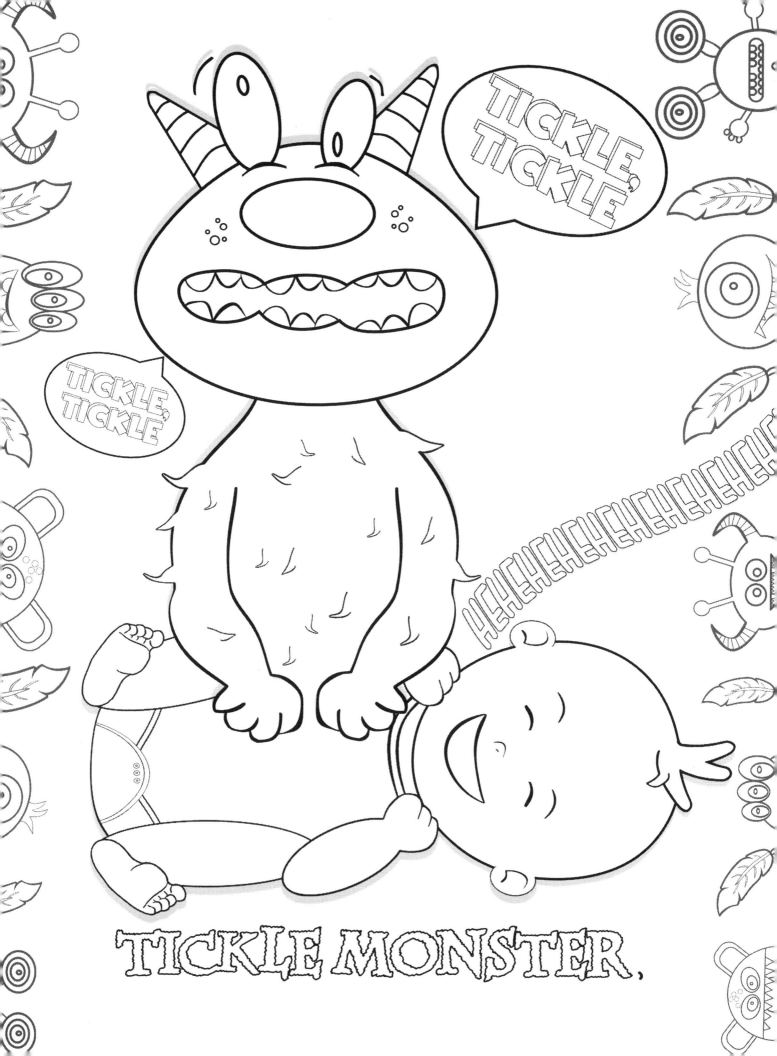

and "How **BIG** is Baby?" game.

SO BIG!

There will be lots of special moments with your baby brother like: The first **BATH**,

And first time **Holding Hands.**

2

← one month «

← birth «

1

It will be so much fun to watch your baby brother GROW!

Draw a picture of your baby brother.

Match the objects to the baby.

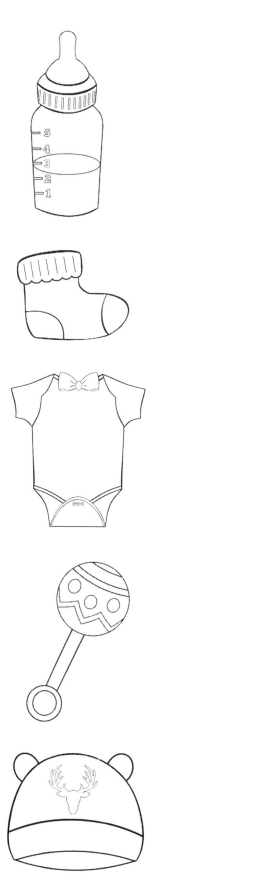
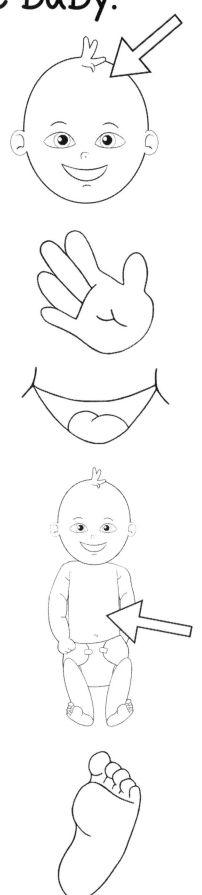

Can you help the baby
find his way to the crib?

I SPY

Find and color the baby items.
Count how many of each picture you found!

Complete the PATTERN.

Look at the pattern below. Use the box to complete the pattern.

DRESS THE BABY

Color the pictures. Cut and paste to dress the baby.

SPOT THE DIFFERENCES

Can you find the 8 differences between the pictures?

COMPLETE THE PICTURE
Draw the missing part of each picture.

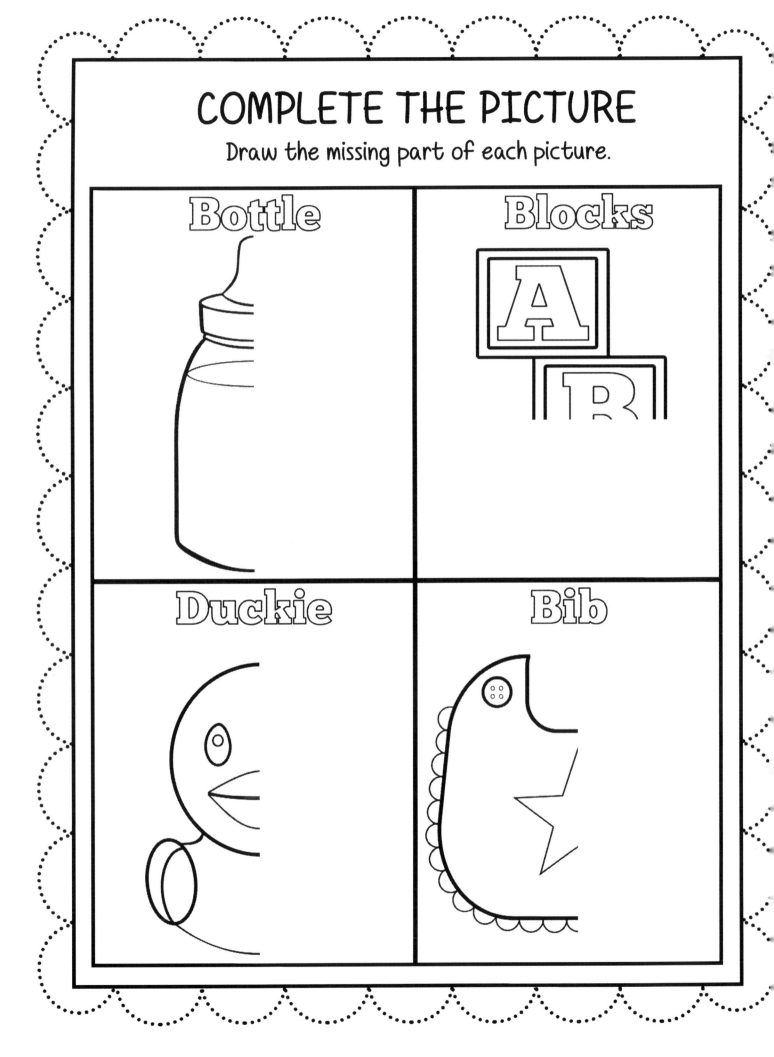

Draw a picture of your whole FAMILY.

Draw a picture of your whole

Tips for Parents

Have the new baby bring the big sister a gift. This can be something small (e.g. a lollipop), but will be memorable for the older sibling.

Include big sister in daily tasks to make her feel like a helper (e.g. picking out diaper or holding the bottle).

During feeding/bathing time for the new baby, provide big sister with coloring/activity book to entertain and relax the older sibling.

Provide positive reinforcement and praise to the big sister.

Ask for help from family, friends, & neighbors!

Made in the USA
Coppell, TX
24 April 2024

31579837R00024